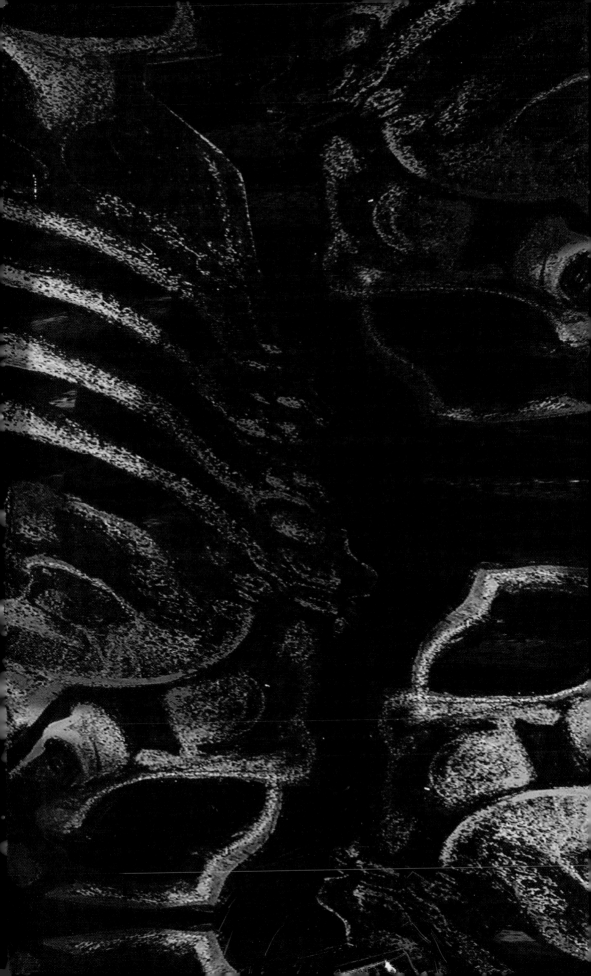

ALIENS VERSUS PREDATOR™
eternal

STORY
Ian Edginton

ART
Alex Maleev

COLOR DESIGN
Perry McNamee

COLOR RENDERING
Dark Horse Digital

LETTERING
Clem Robins

COVER ART
Glenn Fabry

TITAN BOOKS

PUBLISHER
Mike Richardson

SERIES EDITOR
Phil Amara

COLLECTION EDITOR
Chris Warner

COLLECTION DESIGNER
Darcy Hockett

ART DIRECTOR
Mark Cox

ORIGINAL ALIEN DESIGN
H. R. Giger

SPECIAL THANKS TO
Debbie Olshan
AT TWENTIETH CENTURY FOX LICENSING

THIS BOOK COLLECTS ISSUES ONE THROUGH FOUR OF THE
DARK HORSE COMIC-BOOK SERIES ALIENS™ VERSUS PREDATOR™: ETERNAL.

ALIENS™ VERSUS PREDATOR™: ETERNAL

PUBLISHED BY TITAN BOOKS LTD. BY ARRANGEMENT WITH DARK HORSE COMICS, INC. ALIENS™ AND PREDATOR™ ARE TRADEMARKS OF TWENTIETH CENTURY FOX FILM CORPORATION. ALIENS™ IS © 1986, 1999 TWENTIETH CENTURY FOX FILM CORPORATION. PREDATOR™ IS © 1987, 1999 TWENTIETH CENTURY FOX FILM CORPORATION. TEXT AND ILLUSTRATIONS © 1998, 1999 TWENTIETH CENTURY FOX FILM CORPORATION. ALL RIGHTS RESERVED. ALL OTHER MATERIAL, UNLESS OTHERWISE SPECIFIED, © 1999 DARK HORSE COMICS, INC. NO PORTION OF THIS PUB-LICATION MAY BE REPRODUCED OR TRANSMITTED, IN ANY FORM OR BY ANY MEANS, WITHOUT THE EXPRESS, WRITTEN PERMISSION OF DARK HORSE COMICS, INC. NAMES, CHARACTERS, PLACES, AND INCIDENTS FEATURED IN THIS PUBLICATION ARE EITHER THE PRODUCT OF THE AUTHOR'S IMAGINATION OR USED FICTITIOUSLY. ANY RESEMBLANCE TO ACTUAL PERSONS (LIVING OR DEAD), EVENTS, INSTITUTIONS, OR LOCALES, WITHOUT SATIRIC INTENT, IS COINCIDENTAL. DARK HORSE COMICS® AND THE DARK HORSE LOGO ARE TRADEMARKS OF DARK HORSE COMICS, INC., REG-ISTERED IN VARIOUS CATEGORIES AND COUNTRIES. ALL RIGHTS RESERVED.

PUBLISHED BY
TITAN BOOKS LTD.
42-44 DOLBEN STREET
LONDON SE1 0UP

SEPTEMBER 1999
FIRST EDITION
ISBN: 1-84023-111-4

2 4 6 8 10 9 7 5 3 1

PRINTED IN CANADA

LIAR, THIEF, WHORE, MURDERER. LI YAT SEN IS *ALL* OF THESE-- THE LATTER *MOST* RECENTLY.

PLAYING THE WANDERING SAGE, HE PEDDLED ELIXIRS AND UNCTIONS TO DIM-WITTED MOUNTAIN VILLAGERS.

YET EVEN *HE* DIDN'T ANTICIPATE HIS CURE-ALL OF SNAKE BLOOD, GINSENG, AND URINE FERMENTING INTO A TOXIC BREW.

SEVENTEEN DIED...

...THE REST *SMASHED* HIS CHEST LIKE PORCELAIN, DROVE HIM OUT TO A SLOW DEATH, BREATHING HIS OWN BLOOD AS NIGHT AND COLD CLOSED IN.

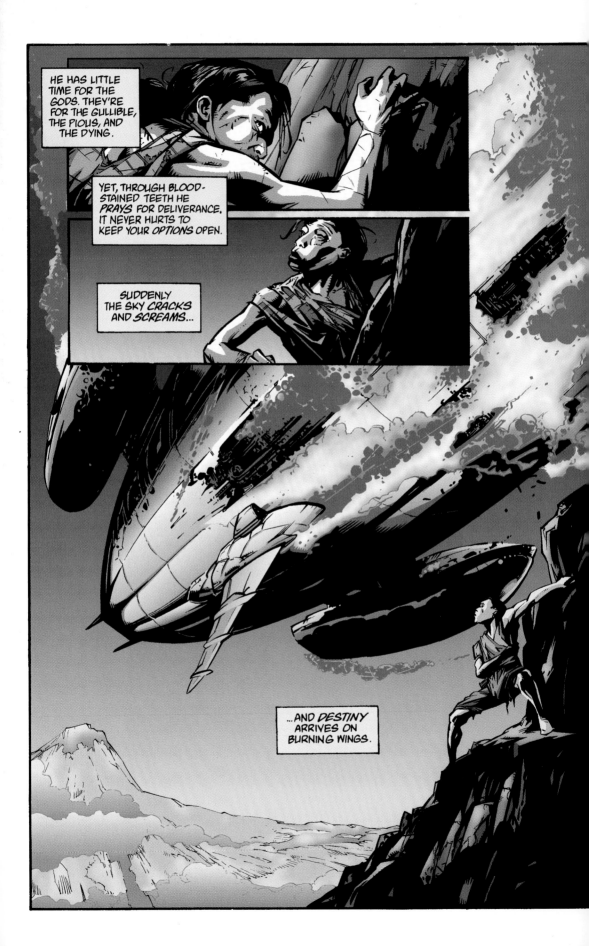

HE HAS LITTLE TIME FOR THE GODS. THEY'RE FOR THE GULLIBLE, THE PIOUS, AND THE DYING.

YET, THROUGH BLOOD-STAINED TEETH HE *PRAYS* FOR DELIVERANCE. IT NEVER HURTS TO KEEP YOUR *OPTIONS* OPEN.

SUDDENLY THE SKY *CRACKS* AND *SCREAMS*...

...AND *DESTINY* ARRIVES ON BURNING WINGS.

THE *SLAUGHTER-HOUSE* OF WEST AFRICA. THAT'S HOW THE *WORLD* HAS COME TO KNOW THIS FORMER FRENCH COLONY OF GAMIBIA.

SINCE ITS INDEPENDENCE THIRTY YEARS AGO, GOVERNMENT FORCES AND COMMUNIST REBELS HAVE FOUGHT A *BLOODY* CIVIL WAR.

UNSPEAKABLE ATROCITIES HAVE BEEN COMMITTED BY *BOTH* SIDES. BUT IT WAS THE *MASSACRE* OF FIFTY AID WORKERS AND JOURNALISTS TEN YEARS AGO THAT *FINALLY* SAW THE WEST *WITHDRAW* ITS AID.

NO NEWS TEAM HAS *DARED* VENTURE BACK INSIDE ITS BORDERS UNTIL *NOW*...

HOLD IT, EARL...THAT COULD BE *HIM*.

"IT *IS*...KEEP ROLLING.

"IN AN *EXCLUSIVE* REPORT, WE REVEAL PRINCE LAURENT MAKAEBA, GRANDSON OF OF FORMER KING FRANCOIS, HAS COME *OUT OF EXILE* IN BERLIN TO DO WHAT THE UNITED NATIONS COULD *NOT*...,

...FORGE A *LASTING* PEACE IN THESE FIELDS OF FIRE.

THIS IS REBECCA MCBRIDE FOR THE INDEPENDENT NEWS NETWORK.

OKAY, THAT'LL DO. I'LL GET A FEW WORDS FROM HIS HIGHNESS AND WE'LL HAVE ENOUGH TO UP-LINK BACK TO LONDON.

THIS TIME TOMORROW WE'LL BE BLOWING OUR *WELL-EARNED* BONUS ON A *SKINFUL* DOWN THE PUB.

CAN'T COME *TOO SOON* NEITHER. THIS PLACE GIVES ME THE WILLIES AN' NO MISTAKE.

"HOLD ON, WHAT'S *THAT?*"

REC: 9.03.41

SHRAKK!

TELL ME YOU *GOT* THAT... OR I *WILL* HAVE TO KILL YOU!

I *GOT* IT! BELIEVE ME, I *GOT* IT...

"...NOW LET'S GET THE HELL *OUT* OF HERE!"

FORGET IT, WE'RE *STAYING!*

BECCA! THE REBELS HAVE *CLEARLY* BROKEN THE TRUCE, THEY'RE GONNA KILL *EVERYONE...* US INCLUDED!

THEN *WHERE* ARE THEY, SMART ARSE? *LOOK* AROUND YOU, NOTICE ANYTHING *MISSING*...LIKE THE BAD GUYS?

COME ON! WE'RE *WORKING.*

I'M *NOT* CUT OUT F' THIS CRAP.

SHRAKK!

ZONE'S CLEAR AND PACIFIED. COLLATERAL DAMAGE IS ONE HUNDRED PERCENT.

GOOD...

...*THREE* MONTHS SINCE YOUR MEN DERAILED THE PEACE PROCESS IN GHAMIBIA, AND STILL *THEY* HAVE NOT MADE AN APPEARANCE!

OH, SO IT'S *MY* FAULT THAT THERE'RE A NO-SHOW? COME ON, LEE, YOU *KNOW* HOW IT WORKS.

THE ENVIRONMENT HAS TO BE JUST *SO* TO LURE THEM OUT... *HEAT* AND *CONFLICT*, RIGHT?

"THREE MONTHS, MAJOR CABOT...

OKAY, SO THEY HAVEN'T TAKEN THE BAIT SO *READILY* THIS TIME. THEY WILL, WE *JUST* HAVE TO BE PATIENT.

MAJOR, MY PATIENCE IS *SHORT* AND *TIME* THE ONE COMMODITY I *NO* LONGER HAVE THE LUXURY OF.

WALK WITH ME.

TEK

"I THINK WE'VE ALL HAD *MORE* THAN ENOUGH EXCITEMENT FOR ONE DAY."

"MY NAME IS *REBECCA MCBRIDE* AND MY LIFE IS *SERIOUSLY* IN THE TOILET.

"SEVENTY-TWO HOURS AGO I WAS IN *GAMBIA*, A PIMPLE ON THE ARSE OF AFRICA WHERE STARCHED UNIFORMED *PSYCHOPATHS* SENT BOY SOLDIERS TO *BUTCHER* EACH OTHER FOR SOME CAUSE OR ANOTHER. I DON'T THINK THEY REALLY *CARED* WHICH.

"ALL *I* CARED ABOUT WAS THE *MAJOR* STORY THAT WAS *BREAKING*. THEIR EXILED MONARCH HAD RETURNED TO NEGOTIATE THE *FIRST* PEACE SETTLEMENT IN *THIRTY* YEARS, AND I WANTED *IN*.

"MY *CAMERAMAN*, EARL, AND I WERE THE *ONLY* NEWS TEAM TO GET THROUGH. NO ONE ELSE WOULD *TOUCH* IT. THERE WERE TOO MANY *JOURNALISTS'* BONES IN THOSE *KILLING* FIELDS ...

"...BUT WHAT THE *HELL*, I WAS BECCA MCBRIDE. I'D GO WHERE CNN AND THE BBC *FEARED* TO TREAD.

"I WAS *MURROW, PILGER* AND *THOMPSON* IN A WONDER BRA AND COMBAT BOOTS. I WAS THE NEW WAVE, THE JOURNALIST AS *ROCK STAR*. I'D EVEN DONE A *PENTHOUSE* SPREAD, FOR CHRISSAKE. I WAS *UNTOUCHABLE*.

"*YEAH, RIGHT...*

"...TAKE IT FROM ME, *NEVER* BELIEVE YOUR *OWN* PRESS.

"*SOMETHING* SLAUGHTERED EARL... THE PRINCE... *EVERYONE.* SOMETHING I *COULDN'T* SEE AND CAN'T EXPLAIN. I GOT LUCKY; A U.N. SWOOP TEAM PULLED ME OUT, *BURNT AND BLEEDING.*

"IN FORTY-EIGHT HOURS I WAS BACK IN LONDON... ABOUT AS *WELCOME* AS A FRENCH KISS AT A *FUNERAL.*

"THE MEDIA FRATERNITY DROPPED ME LIKE A B.S.E. BURGER. MY EGO GOT EARL *KILLED.* I COULDN'T GET *LAID,* LET ALONE A CHANCE TO TELL *MY* SIDE OF THE STORY.

"AND IF I DID, *WHO'D* BELIEVE ME? EARL'S CAMERA, THE TAPES, ALL THE *EVIDENCE* IS GONE...

...WELL, NOT *QUITE* ALL.

THE PERSON OF *DUBIOUS* HYGIENE OVER THERE IS *CRAB*, A TECHNO PAGAN IF YOU'LL EXCUSE THE CONTRADICTION. HIS *REAL* NAME'S JULIAN, AND HIS DAD'S A *STOCKBROKER*, BUT I *DON'T* LET ON I KNOW.

HE AND HIS *COUNTERCULTURE, ANARCHIST,* RICH-KID CHUMS ARE JUST A FEW OF THE WEIRD *CONTACTS* I'VE MADE OVER THE YEARS. THEY'RE INTO VEGANISM, SMART DRUGS, RAVING, AND BEST OF ALL, *TOTAL DATA ACCESS.*

THEY *HACK* CORPORATE AND GOVERNMENTAL *DIRTY LAUNDRY* AND HANG IT OUT ON THE *NET* FOR ALL THE *WORLD* TO SEE."

HERE, BEC, COP A LOAD OF THIS!

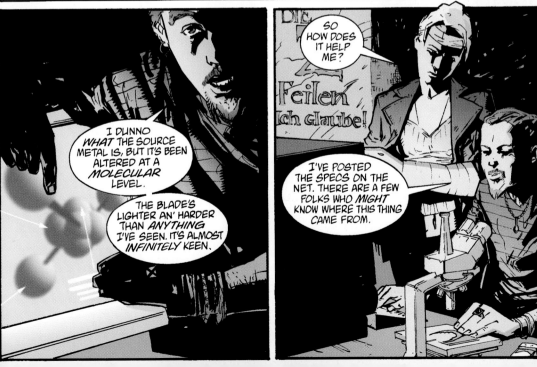

I DUNNO *WHAT* THE SOURCE METAL IS, BUT IT'S BEEN ALTERED AT A *MOLECULAR* LEVEL.

THE BLADE'S LIGHTER AN' HARDER THAN *ANYTHING* I'VE SEEN. IT'S ALMOST *INFINITELY KEEN.*

SO HOW DOES IT HELP ME?

I'VE POSTED THE SPECS ON THE NET. THERE ARE A FEW FOLKS WHO *MIGHT* KNOW WHERE THIS THING CAME FROM.

AND ALL THANKS TO A MOST *UNFORSEEN* TWIST OF FATE.

FATE APPEARS TO BE TWISTING *AGAIN* BUT THIS TIME *NOT* IN MY FAVOR.

I AM *DYING.* EACH DAY I FEEL A LITTLE *MORE* DEATH CREEP INTO MY BONES.

I AM *AFRAID,* BUT AFTER SO LONG I AM *USED* TO THE FEAR NOW. THIS IS NOT THE *FIRST* TIME, NOR WILL IT BE THE *LAST.* THE SECRET IS NOT TO FIGHT *AGAINST* DEATH...

...BUT TO *BEND* TO IT. TO ADAPT...

THEY CAN'T *GET OUT* OF THERE, CAN THEY?

NO, ALL *BIOHAZARD* CONTAINMENT UNITS ARE LINED WITH AN ALLOY DERIVED FROM THE PREDATOR SHIP. IT IS ALMOST IMPENET-RABLE.

ALMOST?

LONDON TO TOKYO, *ECONOMY* DIRECT. IF IT'S NOT A *HUMAN RIGHTS* VIOLATION, IT *BLOODY* WELL SHOULD BE.

I *ACHE* IN PLACES I *NEVER* KNEW I HAD, AND *SMELL* LIKE A *WRESTLER'S ARMPIT*.

...BUT NOW I'M HERE.

I'VE SOLD *EVERYTHING* I OWN AND *MAXED* MY CREDIT CARDS TO INFINITY...

MY *ONLY* CONTACT IS CRAB'S OTAKU FRIEND *LAZARUS*. WITH A BIT OF LUCK AND A FLASH OF THIGH, HE'LL HELP ME DIG UP WHATEVER I NEED TO KNOW ABOUT *GIDEON SUHN LEE*.

IT'S THREE A.M. AND HOTTER THAN A CHERNOBYL SUMMER. AIR CONDITIONING, IN THIS PIT? DREAM ON.

THE TRANSSEXUAL HOOKERS NEXT DOOR ARE PARTYING TO SIBERIAN SPEED METAL. THE FEEDBACK SETS MY FILLINGS ON EDGE. SLEEP'S JUST WISHFUL THINKING, SO I DRAG ON MY FIFTH IRANIAN FILTERLESS AND TRY TO KICK-START MY BRAIN.

WELCOME TO TOKYO.

I WAS HERE LAST IN NINETEEN WHEN THE PACIFIC ECONOMIC BUBBLE BURST. SALARYMEN WERE COMMITTING SEPPUKU ALL OVER. THE ONLY GROWTH INDUSTRY WAS IN INDUSTRIAL OFFICE CLEANERS.

EVENTUALLY, INEVITABLY, THE COUNTRY CRAWLED BACK UP THE FOOD CHAIN AND REASSERTED ITSELF.

OLD CITIES LIKE THIS DON'T DIE. THEY'RE LIVING, URBAN ORGANISMS. SURVIVORS. CUNNING, AMORAL ...

...AND OCCASIONALLY THEY EAT THEIR YOUNG.

RIGHT NOW IT'S A VERITABLE FEEDING FRENZY. PEOPLE ARE BEING SNATCHED, MURDERED, AND MUTILATED. FIFTEEN SO FAR, BUT I SUSPECT THERE'S MORE. HERE'S THE TWIST, THOUGH...

...ALL THE KILLINGS OCCURRED WITHIN A BLOCK OF GIDEON SUHN LEE'S CORPORATE TOWER. HE COULD GOB FROM HIS PENTHOUSE AND HIT A CHALK OUTLINE.

THE FIRST CORPSE TURNED UP A DAY AFTER THE EXPLOSION AT SAID TOWER. A MINOR LAB ACCIDENT, HIS SPIN TEAM SAID. FAMILIES OF THE DEAD AND INJURED SIGNED EXTENSIVE NON DISCLO-SURE COMPENSATION DEALS WITHIN THE HOUR.

I'D ARRIVED HERE TRAILING CLUES TO ONE MYSTERY AND STUMBLED OVER ANOTHER. AND TIED UP IN THEM BOTH IS THE ENIGMATIC MISTER LEE.

MY DAD USED TO SAY I WAS ALWAYS ONE TO GO LOOKING FOR TROUBLE, JUMPING OUT OF THE FRYING PAN AND INTO THE FIRE...

...WELL, RIGHT ABOUT NOW, IT FEELS LIKE SOMEONE'S TURNING UP THE HEAT.

KKHSSSS

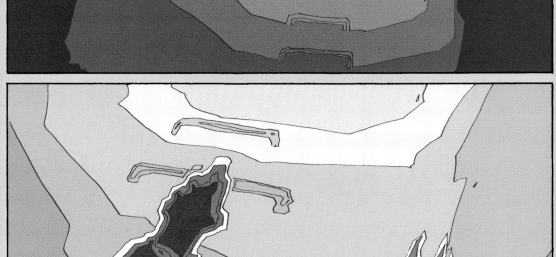

THEY SAID IT WAS A
GAS MAIN EXPLOSION.
A TERRIBLE, TRAGIC
ACCIDENT...

OTAKU ARE DATA FREAKS, OBSESSIVE ACQUIRERS OF USELESS INFO ON SPECIFIC SUBJECTS-- JEWISH PORN STARS, SPETNATZ HANDGUNS, VANILLA ICE, THE WOMBLES...

...LAZARUS LIKES SECRETS. PERSONAL, INDUSTRIAL, GOVERNMENTAL, YOU NAME IT. THAT'S WHY HE'S SO ANAL ABOUT NOT MEETING. HIS SECURITY'S HIS LIFE.

SUBWAY

HE'S BEEN TRAWLING FOR DATA ON LEE FOR ME AND IT LOOKS LIKE HE'S FOUND SOMETHING...

...SOMETHING HE DOESN'T TRUST SENDING VIA MODEM. HE WANTS TO MEET!

MY MATE CRAB'S FRIEND, LAZARUS, HAS BEEN DIGGING UP THE DIGITAL DIRT FOR ME. HE'S LOCAL BUT WE'VE NEVER MET. LIKE MOST OTAKU HE'S PROBABLY A GRUBBY AGORAPHOBIC RAISED ON JUNK FOOD AND TRASH TV.

THEY'VE OPTED OUT OF JAPANESE SOCIETY AND ITS HELLISH WEB OF SOCIAL LOYALTIES AND OBLIGA- TIONS. THEY ONLY INTERACT WITH OTHERS VIA COMPUTER.

TWENTY-FIRST CENTURY HERMITS. ISN'T TECHNOLOGY MARVELOUS! CHARLIE BABBAGE AND ALAN TURING MUST BE SPINNING IN THEIR GRAVES LIKE TOPS!

WHY DOES THAT SCARE ME?

"HOW DO YOU FEEL, MAJOR CABOT?"

HEART RATE

BLOOD TYPE

CHOLESTEROL COUNT

WELL ENOUGH, I GUESS. CORNELL DIED THIS MORNING. THAT MAKES THREE SO FAR.

OUT OF A TEAM OF HOW MANY? FIVE? SIX?

THERE WERE ONLY THE TWO PREDATORS, WEREN'T THERE, MAJOR?

IS THERE A POINT TO THIS?

PREPARE THE BETA RESERVE. YOU'RE GOING HUNTING AGAIN, SOON.

LATER

I'VE GOT TO HAND IT TO HIM, HE'S SHREWD.

IN THIS PART OF TOWN NO ONE WOULD THINK TWICE ABOUT A JAPANESE GUY BEING SEEN WITH A EUROPEAN HOSTESS.

BEEPBEEP

UH-OH. DON'T SAY HE'S CRYING OFF.

behind you

BEHIND YOU? WHAT'S HE PLAYING AT...

YOU *BASTARD!* YOU *MURDERED* EARL AND *SCREWED* UP MY LIFE ALL FOR SOME BLOODY *TEST!!*

OH, *PLEASE!* I THREW *DOWN* THE CHALLENGE, YOU WEREN'T *OBLIGED* TO TAKE IT UP.

I EVEN LEFT *CLUES.* THE SPEAR TIP? LAZARUS?

FORGET IT! I'VE HAD ENOUGH. AT LEAST I'VE *SOME* MORALS LEFT.

REALLY?

GOD DAMN YOU...WHAT DO I DO?

"WHAT WAS I *SUPPOSED* TO DO? HE HAD ME, AND HE *KNEW* IT.

"SIX HOURS LATER WE WERE UNDERGROUND.

"HE WANTED TO *CAPTURE* ONE ALIVE AND USE IT AS *BAIT.*

"A SALARYMAN HAD BEEN SNATCHED OFF A BULLET TRAIN PLATFORM BY THE REMAINING *CREATURE* THAT HAD *ESCAPED* FROM LEE'S LAB.

"APPARENTLY THIS NECK OF THE WOODS WAS ITS GAME TRAIL. *THE PREDATORS* HAD *SLAUGHTERED* ONE AND SEEMED INTENT ON HUNTING THE OTHER. SO WAS *LEE.*

"WE HAD THE PLACE TO OURSELVES. HIS PEOPLE HAD *FAKED* A TERRORIST WARNING ABOUT RELEASING *HALLUCINOGENIC* GAS INTO THE SUBWAY. IT MADE YOU SEE *MONSTERS.* CUTE.

I'D GUESS OUR FRIENDS HAVE ACCESS TO *OTHER* VISUAL FREQUENCIES *BESIDE* INFRARED.

I KNOW A WAY OF EVENING THE ODDS.

PAFF

THESE GUYS DON'T HUNT IN HOT *DRY* PLACES JUST SO THEY CAN WORK ON THEIR *TAN!*

FFSSSSS

BRAVO! SUCH SAVAGE GRACE, SUCH PRIMAL FEROCITY. YOU HAVE SO MUCH *LIFE* IN YOU...

...AND IT'S ALL *MINE*.

COME, *DRAGON*. YOUR TIME IS *DONE*, LET'S END THIS...

...IN THE OLD WAY.

CHIKCHAK

SSSS

...DRAGON!!...

"I COULD *SCREAM*. THERE ARE *THINGS* FROM OTHER WORLDS FIGHTING TO THE *DEATH* RIGHT IN FRONT OF ME. IMAGINE *THAT* ON THE SIX O'CLOCK NEWS--

SSSSS

"-- I JUST WISH I HAD A *CAMERA*.

"THEN IT HITS ME...*EARL*.

SLUK

"POOR STUPID, SCARED EARL. WHAT *DID* I DO TO YOU? I GOT YOU KILLED FOR *RATINGS*, THAT'S WHAT. CABOT WAS *RIGHT*.

"WHAT A BITCH."

"SO, I GUESS THIS IS *MY* PAYBACK."

HSSSs

AHHH!!

KSSSs

NO, NOT LIKE THIS!

"CABOT'S GUN!"

"I CAME TO IN A HOSPITAL A WEEK LATER. SEEMS SOMEONE OR SOMETHING HAD CARRIED ME UP TO STREET LEVEL BEFORE I BLED TO DEATH."

"AN AGENT FROM *UNIT K* VISITED ME *EACH DAY*, GENTLY PRESSURING ME FOR DETAILS. FAT CHANCE."

"AS I'D EXPECTED, LEE'S PERSONAL AND PRIVATE ASSETS HAD BEEN SEIZED BY THE *GOVERNMENT*. THEY *DENIED* THE EXISTENCE OF HIS PREDATOR ARCHIVE AND THE SPACECRAFT."

"I RETURNED TO LONDON A *MILLIONAIRE*, LEE'S POSTHUMOUS PAYMENT FOR HIS BIOGRAPHY. I GAVE EARL'S FOLKS HALF"

"LEE MAY HAVE BEEN A *MADMAN*, BUT AT LEAST HE WAS A *RICH* MADMAN.

"*NOW* I'M USING MY WINDFALL TO DIG FOR THE *TRUTH*, AND I'VE HIRED CRAB AND HIS TECHNO-PAGAN CHUMS TO HELP ME.

"THERE ARE *MONSTERS* OUT THERE IN THE DARK CORNERS OF THE WORLD. *THINGS* THAT HUNT MEN FOR *SPORT*.

"WHO ARE THEY? WHERE DO THEY COME FROM? WHAT DO THEY *REALLY* WANT?

"IT'S THE STORY OF A LIFETIME, OF *MANY* LIFETIMES, AND ONE WAY OR THE OTHER IT'S *MINE* FOR THE TELLING."

ALIENS™ VERSUS PREDATOR™ eternal

GALLERY

FEATURING THE ORIGINAL SERIES COVER PAINTINGS BY GLENN FABRY.

STAR WARS

CRIMSON EMPIRE
Richardson • Stradley
Gulacy • Russell
160-page color paperback
ISBN: 1-84023-006-1

EPISODE 1—
THE PHANTOM MENACE
Gilroy • Damaggio • Williamson
112-page color paperback
ISBN: 1-84023-025-8

THE LAST COMMAND
Baron • Biukovic • Shanower
144-page color paperback
ISBN: 1-84023-007-X

MARA JADE:
BY THE EMPEROR'S HAND
Zahn • Stackpole • Ezquerra
144-page color paperback
ISBN: 1-84023-011-8

TALES OF THE JEDI: THE
GOLDEN AGE OF THE SITH
Anderson • Gossett
Carrasco • Heike • Black
Beckett • Woch
144-page color paperback
ISBN: 1-84023-000-2

X-WING ROGUE SQUADRON:
THE WARRIOR PRINCESS
Stackpole • Tolson
Nadeau • Ensign
96-page color paperback
ISBN: 1-85286-997-6

X-WING ROGUE SQUADRON:
REQUIEM FOR A ROGUE
Stackpole • Strnad • Erskine
112-page color paperback
ISBN: 1-84023-026-6

X-WING ROGUE SQUADRON:
IN THE EMPIRE'S SERVICE
Stackpole • Nadeau • Ensign
96-page color paperback
ISBN: 1-84023-008-8

X-WING ROGUE SQUADRON:
BLOOD AND HONOR
Stackpole • Crespo
Hall • Johnson
96-page color paperback
ISBN: 1-84023-010-X

ALIENS

FEMALE WAR
(formerly Aliens: Earth War)
Verheiden • Kieth
112-page color paperback
ISBN: 1-85286-784-1

GENOCIDE
Arcudi • Willis • Story
112-page color paperback
ISBN: 1-85286-805-8

HARVEST
(formerly Aliens: Hive)
Prosser • Jones
128-page color paperback
ISBN: 1-85286-838-4

LABYRINTH
Woodring • Plunkett
136-page color paperback
ISBN: 1-85286-844-9

NIGHTMARE ASYLUM
(formerly Aliens: Book Two)
Verheiden • Beauvais
112-page color paperback
ISBN: 1-85286-765-5

OUTBREAK
(formerly Aliens: Book One)
Verheiden • Nelson
168-page color paperback
ISBN: 1-85286-756-6

ROGUE
Edginton • Simpson
112-page color paperback
ISBN: 1-85286-851-1

STRONGHOLD
Arcudi • Mahnke • Palmiotti
112-page color paperback
ISBN: 1-85286-875-9

ALIENS VS PREDATOR

ALIENS VS PREDATOR
Stradley • Norwood • Warner
Story • Campanella
176-page color paperback
ISBN: 1-85286-413-3

THE DEADLIEST
OF THE SPECIES
Claremont • Guice • Barreto
320-page color paperback
ISBN: 1-85286-953-4

WAR
various
200-page color paperback
ISBN: 1-85286-703-5

BATMAN VS PREDATOR

BATMAN VS PREDATOR
Gibbons • Kubert • Kubert
96-page color paperback
ISBN: 1-85286-446-X

BATMAN VS PREDATOR II:
BLOODMATCH
Moench• Gulacy • Austin
136-page color paperback
ISBN: 1-85286-667-5

BATMAN VS PREDATOR III:
BLOOD TIES
Dixon • Damaggio
136-page color paperback
ISBN: 1-85286-913-5

BUFFY THE VAMPIRE
SLAYER

THE DUST WALTZ
Brereton • Gomez
80-page color paperback
ISBN: 1-84023-057-6

THE REMAINING SUNLIGHT
Watson • Van Meter
Bennett • Ross • Ketcham
88-page color paperback
ISBN: 1-84023-078-9

THE ORIGIN
Golden • Brereton
Bennett • Ketcham
80-page color paperback
ISBN: 1-84023-105-X

PREDATOR

BIG GAME
Arcudi • Dorkin • Gil
112-page color paperback
ISBN: 1-85286-454-0

COLD WAR
Verheiden • Randall • Mitchell
112-page color paperback
ISBN: 1-85286-576-8

KINDRED
Lamb • Tolson
112-page color paperback
ISBN: 1-85286-908-9

VARIOUS

BATMAN/ALIENS
Marz • Wrightson
128-page color paperback
ISBN: 1-85286-887-2

PREDATOR VS
JUDGE DREDD
Wagner • Alcatena
80-page color paperback
ISBN: 1-84023-021-5

TARZAN VS PREDATOR
AT THE EARTH'S CORE
Simonson • Weeks
104-page color paperback
ISBN: 1-85286-888-0

**All publications are available through most good bookshops or
direct from our mail-order service at Titan Books. For a free
graphic-novels catalogue or to order, telephone 01858 433 169
with your credit-card details or contact Titan Books Mail Order,
Bowden House, 36 Northampton Road, Market Harborough, Leics,
LE16 9HE, quoting reference BOR/GN.**